Karl
Jenkins

Ryers Down

Flute & piano

Boosey & Hawkes Music Publishers Ltd
www.boosey.com

Written for the flautist Emma Halnan,
winner of The Arts Club – Sir Karl Jenkins Music Award 2016

This work was first performed on 17 May 2016 at 1901 Arts Club, London,
by Emma Halnan (flute) and Daniel King Smith (piano)

COMPOSER'S NOTE

For the first ten years of this century, I lived and composed on the Gower Peninsula,
an area of sandy beaches and dramatic cliff scenery with coastal caves; the first area in
the UK to be officially designated as one of outstanding natural beauty. Living in an old
mill alongside the Bury Pill stream, I wrote from a stable block, enjoying a vista across
Cheriton Valley and the river to Ryers Down. This work is a musical reflection of time
spent there.

KJ

Duration: 5 minutes

Published by Boosey & Hawkes Music Publishers Ltd
Aldwych House
71–91 Aldwych
London
WC2B 4HN

www.boosey.com

© Copyright 2016 by Boosey & Hawkes Music Publishers Ltd

ISMN 979-0-060-13300-8
ISBN 978-1-78454-260-3

First impression 2017

Printed by Halstan:
Halstan UK, 2–10 Plantation Road, Amersham, Bucks, HP6 6HJ. United Kingdom
Halstan DE, Weißliliengasse 4, 55116 Mainz. Germany

Music origination by Jon Bunker

for Emma Halnan

RYERS DOWN

KARL JENKINS
(b 1944)

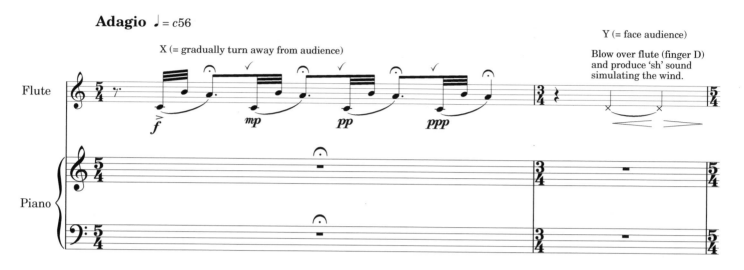

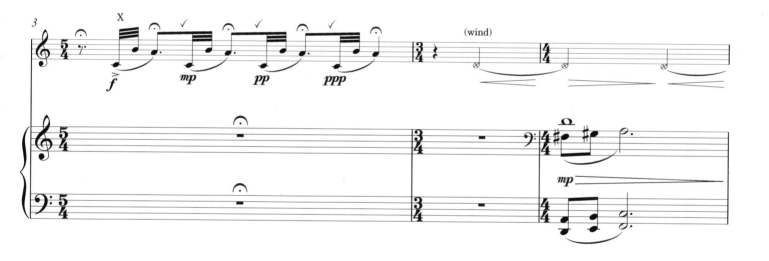

19719

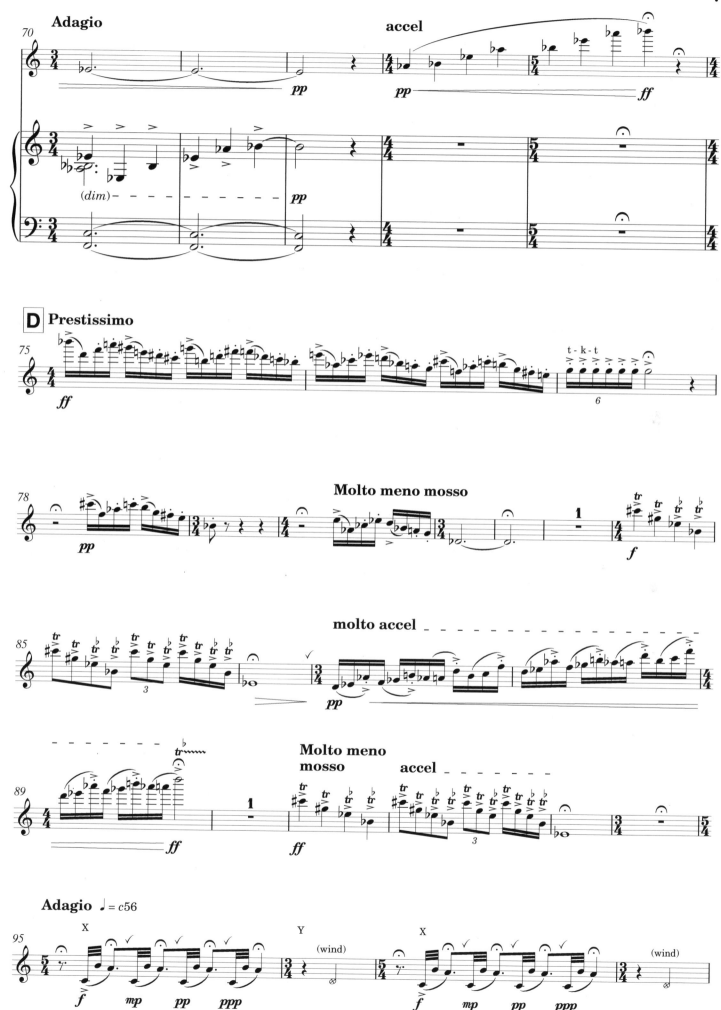

inside piano:
gliss LH from any convenient
string and 'ping' D with RH

ISBN 978-1-78454-260-3

9 781784 542603

ISMN 979-0-060-13300-8

9 790060 133008

BOOSEY & HAWKES

AN IMAGEM COMPANY